GW00672232

Published by

Wise Publications

14-15 Berners Street, London W1T 3LJ, UK.

Order No. AM985050

ISBN 1-84609-456-9

Compiled by Nick Crispin

Cover designed by Chloë Alexander

Printed in the EU

Exclusive Distributors:

Music Sales Limited

Distribution Centre, Newmarket Road, Bury St Edmunds, Suffolk IP33 3YB, UK.

Music Sales Pty Limited

120 Rothschild Avenue, Rosebery, NSW 2018, Australia.

This book © Copyright 2006

Wise Publications, a division of Music Sales Limited.

www.musicsales.com

Wise Publications

part of The Music Sales Group

London/New York/Paris/Sydney/Copenhagen/Berlin/Madrid/Tokyo

1
50 Ways To Leave Your Lover

Words & Music by Paul Simon

"The prob-lem is all in - side your head", she said to me;
She said, "It grieves me now to see you in such pain; I wish there was

"The an-swer is eas - y if you take it log - i - c'lly.
some - thin' I could do to make you smile a - gain."

I'm here to help you if you're strug-glin' to be free; there must be
I said, "I ap - pre-ci-ate that, and could you please ex - plain a - bout the

fif - ty ways to leave your lov-er."
fif-ty ways?"
She said, "it's real-ly not my
She said, "Why don't we both just

hab - it to in - trude; I hope my mean - ing won't be
sleep on it to - night; I'm sure in the morn - ing you'll be-

lost or mis - con-strued. But I'll re-peat my - self at the
-gin to see the light." And then she kissed me and I re - al- ized she

risk of be-ing crude; there must be   fif - ty ways to leave your lov-er,
prob-a -bly was right; there must be   fif - ty ways to leave your lov-er,

fif - ty ways to leave your lov - er." } Just slip out the   back   Jack;
fif - ty ways to leave your lov - er." }

make a new plan, Stan;   you don't need to be coy, Roy,

{ Just get your-self free. }
{ Just lis-ten to   me.   }   Hop on   the bus, Gus;

you don't need to dis-cuss ___ much; ___ Just drop off the key, Lee,

Last time
To Coda ⊕ |1 G

|2 G

and get your-self free.   Slip out the   free.

D.%. al Coda
(with repeats)

⊕ CODA G

free.

3

2
The 59th Street Bridge Song (Feelin' Groovy)

Words & Music by Paul Simon

rhymes for me? Doot-in' doo - doo, feel-in' groov - y.

Ba da da da da da da feel - in' groov - y.

Got no deeds to do, no prom-is-es to keep, I'm dap-pled and drowsy and

read - y to sleep, let the morn-ing time drop all its pet - als on me.

Life, I love you, All is groov - y. _____

Repeat to fade

Ba da da da da da da Ba da da da da.

3
American Pie

Words & Music by Don McLean

A long, long time a-go — I can still re-mem-ber how that mu-sic used to make me smile

And I knew if I had my chance that I could make those peo-ple dance and

may-be they'd be hap-py for a while. But Feb-ru-ar-y made me shiv-er

with ev-'ry pa-per I'd de-liv-er. Bad news on the door-step I could-n't take one more step I

can't re-mem-ber if I cried when I read a-bout his wid-owed bride.

Some-thing touched me deep in-side the day the mu-sic died. —

In a moderate tempo

So bye - bye, Miss A-mer-i-can Pie— Drove my Chev-y to the lev-ee but the

lev-ee was dry. — Them good ole boys — were drink-in' whis-key and rye — Sing-in'

this-'ll be the day that I die, This-'ll be the day that I die.

1. Did you write the book of love and do you have faith in God a-bove?

If the Bi - ble tells you so Now do you be - lieve in

rock and roll. Can mu-sic save your mor-tal soul and can you teach me how to dance

real slow? Well, I know that you're in love with him 'cause I

saw you danc-in' in the gym, You both kicked off your shoes. Man, I dig those rhy-thm and

blues. I was a lone - ly teen - age bronc - in' buck with a pink car - na - tion and a

pick-up truck. But I knew I was out of luck the day the mu-

-sic died. ___ I start-ed sing-ing ___ He was sing-ing ___ bye - bye, Miss A -

mer - i - can Pie ___ Drove my Chev-y to the lev - ee but the lev - ee was dry ___ Them

good ole boys ___ were drink-in' whi-sky and rye ___ Sing - in' this-'ll be the day ___ that I ___ die,

This - 'll be the day ___ that I ___ die ___ I met a girl who sang ___ the blues ___ and

I asked her for some hap-py news, ___ But she just smiled and turned a - way. ___

I went down to the sa-cred store ___ where I heard the mu - sic years be-fore But the

man there said the mu-sic would-n't play. _____ And in the streets the chil - dren screamed, ___ the

lov-ers cried and the po-ets dreamed. But not a word was spo-ken the church bells all were bro-ken. And the

8

three men I ad-mire most, the Fa - ther, Son and the Ho-ly Ghost, They caught the last train for the coast the

day   the   mu - sic   died.   And they were sing - in'. ___

CODA

This - 'll   be   the   day ___ that   I ___   die. _____

2.
Now for ten years we've been on our own, and moss grows fat on a rollin' stone
But that's not how it used to be when the jester sang for the king and queen
In a coat he borrowed from James Dean and a voice that came from you and me
Oh and while the king was looking down, the jester stole his thorny crown
The courtroom was adjourned, no verdict was returned
And while Lenin read a book on Marx the quartet practised in the park
And we sang dirges in the dark
The day the music died
We were singin'... bye-bye... etc.

3.
Helter-skelter in the summer swelter the birds flew off with a fallout shelter
Eight miles high and fallin' fast, it landed foul on the grass
The players tried for a forward pass, with the jester on the sidelines in a cast
Now the half-time air was sweet perfume while the sergeants played a marching tune
We all got up to dance but we never got the chance
'Cause the players tried to take the field, the marching band refused to yield
Do you recall what was revealed
The day the music died
We started singin'... bye-bye... etc.

4.
And there we were all in one place, a generation lost in space
With no time left to start again
So come on, Jack be nimble, Jack be quick, Jack Flash sat on a candlestick
'Cause fire is the devil's only friend
And as I watched him on the stage my hands were clenched in fists of rage
No angel born in hell could break that Satan's spell
And as the flames climbed high into the night to light the sacrificial rite
I saw Satan laughing with delight the day the music died.
He was singin'... bye-bye... etc.

9

4
Angie

Words & Music by Mick Jagger & Keith Richards

⊕ *Coda*

Dm   Am

An - gie,___   I still love you ba - by,___

Dm   Am   Dm

ev'ry-where I look_ I see your eyes._____   There ain't a wo-man that_ comes

Am   C   F   G

close to you,   come on, ba - by, dry your eyes._____

Am   E⁷   G   F

An - gie,_   An - gie,   ain't it good_ to be a - live?__
An - gie,_   An - gie,   you can't say_ we nev- er tried.__

1.
B♭/F   F   C   E⁷/B

2.
B♭/F   F   C

Verse 2:
Angie, you're beautiful,
But ain't it time we said goodbye?
Angie, I still love you,
Remember all those nights we cried?
All the dreams we held so close
Seemed to all go up in smoke,
Let me whisper in your ear:
"Angie, Angie",
Where will it lead us from here?

Verse 3:
Instrumental
Oh, Angie, don't you weep,
Ah, your kisses still taste sweet.
I hate that sadness in your eyes,
But Angie, Angie,
Ain't it time we said goodbye?

11

5
Angels

Words & Music by Robbie Williams & Guy Chambers

when love is dead,   I'm lov-ing an-gels in-stead.   And through it   all___

D.S. al Coda

✆ *Coda*

And through it   all_____ she of-fers me__pro-tec-tion,   a lot of love and af-fec-

- tion   whe-ther I'm right or wrong.   And down the wa - ter-fall_____ wher-ev-er it   may take_

___ me,   I know that life__ won't break__ me,___   when I   come   to call,

she won't for-sake__ me,   I'm lov-ing an-gels in-stead.

6
Babylon

Words & Music by David Gray

Capo first fret

♩ = 76

1. Fri-day night_ an' I'm go-in' no - where, all the lights_ are chang-in' green_ to red.

Turn-in' ov - er T._ V. sta-tions, si-tu-a - tions run-nin' through_ my_ head.

Look-in' back_ through time you know it's clear_ that I've_ been blind, I've_ been a fool._

To o - pen up_ my heart_ to all_ that jeal-ous - y,_ that bit-ter-ness,_ that_

_ rid - i - cule.

2. Sat - ur - day,_ I'm run-nin' wild, an' all_ the lights_ are chang - in' red_
3. Sun-day all,_ the lights in Lon - don, shin-ing sky_ is fad - ing red_

_ to green._
_ to blue._

Mov - in' through_ the clouds, _ I'm push - in',
Kick - in' through_ the aut - umn leaves an'

7
Blackbird

Words & Music by John Lennon & Paul McCartney

1. Black-bird sing-ing in the dead of night,__
2. Black-bird sing-ing in the dead of night,__
(3° Instrumental)

__ take these bro-ken wings__ and learn to fly;__
__ take these sunk-en eyes__ and learn to see;__

all your life_____ you were on-ly wait-ing for this mo-ment to a-
all your life_____ you were on-ly wait-ing for this mo-ment to be

- rise.   free.

Black - bird,__ fly,_____   Black - bird,__ fly,

8
Blowin' In The Wind

Words & Music by Bob Dylan

9
Both Sides Now

Words & Music by Joni Mitchell

10
Bridge Over Troubled Water

Words & Music by Paul Simon

11
Brown Eyed Girl

Words & Music by Van Morrison

12
California Dreamin'

Words & Music by John Phillips & Michelle Phillips

I passed a-long the way. Well, I got down on my knees, *Got down on my knees* and I pre-tend to pray *I pre-tend to pray*

you know the preach-er likes the cold, *Preach-er likes the cold,* He knows I'm gon-na stay. *Knows I'm gon-na stay.* Ca-li-for-nia dream-in', *Ca-li-for-nia dreamin'*

on such a win-ter's day. *on such a win-ter's day.* All the leaves are

on such a win-ter's day. *on such a win-ter's, Cal-i-forn-ia dream-in',* on such a win-ter's *on such a win-ter's,*

Cal-i-forn-ia dream-in', on such a win-ter's day. *on such a win-ter's day.*

27

13
Bye Bye Love

Words & Music by Felice & Boudleaux Bryant

14
A Case Of You

Words & Music by Joni Mitchell

- da,_____ with your__ face__ sketched on it____ twice. Oh,

you are in my___blood like ho - ly wine,_____ you taste so bit - ter__ and so sweet. Oh,

I could drink a case__ of___ you,_____ dar - ling, and I would

still__ be on my feet, oh, I would still be on_____ my___ feet._____

1.

To Coda

(Guitar)

Oh,_____

___ I am a lone - ly paint - er,____ I live in a box___ of paints,____

I'm fright - ened_____ by_____ the de - vil, and I'm

drawn to those ones____ that ain't__ a - fraid._____ I re - mem-

-ber that_ time_ you told_ me, you said "Love is touch-ing___ souls."_

Sure-ly you touched mine__ 'cos part of you pours out_ of me__

__ in these lines___ from time to time._ Oh,

I met a wo-man,_ she had___ a mouth_ like yours,_ she knew your life,_

she knew your de - vils and your de - mons._ And she said,

"Go___ to him, stay with him if you can,_

but be_ pre-pared_ to bleed."___ Oh,_

(Guitar)

31

15
The Circle Game

Words & Music by Joni Mitchell

Verse 3:
Sixteen springs and sixteen summers gone now
Cartwheels turn to car wheels thru the town
And they tell him,
Take your time, it won't be long now
Till you drag your feet to slow the circles down.
And the seasons they go round and round, *etc.*

Verse 4:
So the years spin by and now the boy is twenty
Though his dreams have lost some grandeur coming true
There'll be new dreams, maybe better dreams and plenty
Before the last revolving year is through.
And the seasons they go round and round, *etc.*

16
The Closest Thing To Crazy

Words & Music by Mike Batt

clos-est thing_ to cra-zy I have ev - er been. Feel-ing twen-ty two,_ act-ing

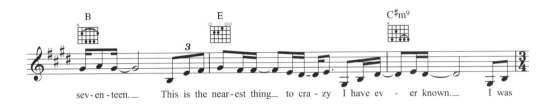

sev-en-teen._ This is the near-est thing_ to cra-zy I have ev - er known._ I was

nev-er cra - zy on my own_ and now I know_ that there's a link be-tween_ the two._

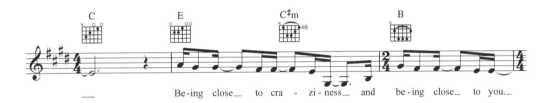

_ Be-ing close_ to cra - zi-ness_ and be-ing close_ to you._

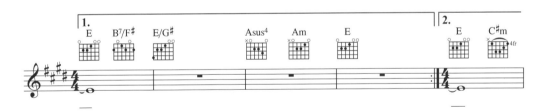

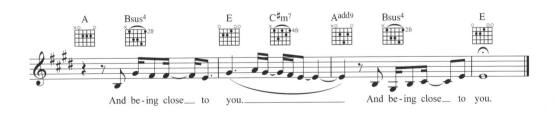

And be-ing close_ to you._ And be-ing close_ to you.

17
Constant Craving

Words & Music by k.d. lang & Ben Mink

37

18
Corcovado
(Quiet Nights Of Quiet Stars)

Words & Music by Antonio Carlos Jobim

19
Crazy

Words & Music by Willie Nelson

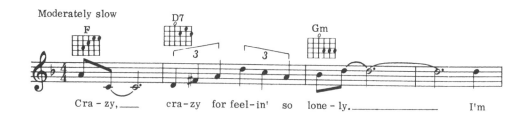

Moderately slow

Cra - zy, ___ cra - zy for feel-in' so lone - ly. ___ I'm

cra - zy, ___ cra - zy for feel - in' so blue. ___

I knew ___ you'd love me as long as you want - ed, ___ And then

some - day, ___ you'd leave me for some - bod - y new. ___

Wor-ry,_____ why do I let my-self wor-ry._____

Won-d'rin',_ what in the world did I do?_____

Cra-zy,_____ for think-ing that my love could hold you,_____ I'm

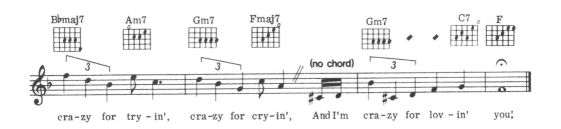

cra-zy for try-in', cra-zy for cry-in', And I'm cra-zy for lov-in' you!

20
A Day In The Life

Words & Music by John Lennon & Paul McCartney

I read the news to-day___ oh boy
He blew his mind out in ___ a car
I saw a film to-day___ oh boy
I heard the news to-day___ oh boy

A - bout a luck - y man who made the grade
He did - n't no - tice that the lights had changed
The Eng - lish arm - y had just won the war
Four thou-sand holes in Black-burn Lan - ca -shire

And though the news___ was ra - ther sad
A crowd of peo - ple stood and stared
A crowd of peo - ple turned a - way
And though the holes___ were ra - ther small

Well I just had to laugh - augh ___
They'd seen his face be - fore___
But I just had to look___
They had to count them all ___

I saw the pho - to-graph - aph

No-bo-dy was real-ly sure If he was from the House of Lords ___   Hav-ing read the

book   I'd love to turn _____ you _____ on _____

Woke up   got   out of bed   Dragged a

comb a-cross my head _ Found my way down stairs and drank a cup And

look-ing up   I no-ticed I was late   Found my

coat and grabbed my hat _   Made the bus in se-conds flat _

Found my   way up-stairs and had a   smoke _   And

D.S. al Coda 𝄌

Some-bo-dy spoke and I went in-to a dream.

Coda

Now they know how ma-ny holes it takes to fill the Al-bert Hall.   I'd

love to turn _____ you _____ on.

43

21
Diamonds And Rust

Words & Music by Joan Baez

lou-sy, you said._ Where are you call - ing from? A booth in the mid west._____

Ten_ years a - go I bought you_ some cuff links._____ You_ brought me

some-thing.__ We both know what mem-'ries can bring: They bring dia-monds and rust. 2. Well,

Now I see____you stand-ing with brown leaves fall-ing all a-round and snow in your

hair. Now you're smil - ing out the win-dow of that crum-my ho-tel o - ver Wa-shing-ton

Square. Our breath__ comes out, white clouds, ming-les and hangs_ in the air.

___ Speak-ing strict-ly for me, we both could have died_ then and there.

Repeat to fade

45

22
Don't Know Why

Words & Music by Jesse Harris

I wished that I_____ could fly_____ a - way,_____ 'stead of kneel - ing in
I_____ will die_____ in ec - sta - sy,_____ but I'll be_____ a bag

the sand, catch - ing tear - drops in my_____ hand._)
of bones, driv - ing down_ the road a - lone._____) My

heart is_____ drenched in_____ wine._____

But you'll be_____ on_____ my_____ mind_

for_____ ev - er._____ - er._____

D.S. al Coda

Coda

don't know why___ I did-n't come. I_____ don't know why I did - n't come.___

rit.

47

Don't Leave Home

Words & Music by Dido Armstrong & Rollo Armstrong

1. Like a ghost,__ don't need a key.__ Your best__ __friend I've come to be.__ And please don't think of get-ting up__ __ for__ me,__ you don't ev - en need to speak.

2. And I've been__ here for just__ one day,__ you'll al-rea-dy miss__ __ me if I go a-way.

3. And I ar - rived when you__ were weak, I'll make you weak-er, like a child.

So close the blinds and shut the door.__

Now all your love you give to me.__

You won't need o-ther friends__ a-ny-more.

When your__ heart_____ is all I need.

Oh,_____ don't leave home. Oh,_____ don't__ leave

24
Everything I Own

Words & Music by David Gates

some-one you know_ that won't let you go,_ and tak-ing it all_ for grant-ed? You may

lose them one day,_ some-one takes them a-way,_ and you don't hear a word they

say. And I would give an - y-thing_ I own,_ give up my life, my heart,_ my home._

_ And I would give an - y - thing_ I own_ just to

have_ you_ back_ a-gain, just to talk to you once_ a-gain.

Is there

- y-thing_ I own,_ give up my life, my heart,_ my home._ And I would give an-

25
Father And Son

Words & Music by Cat Stevens

53

26
Fernando

Words & Music by Benny Andersson, Bjorn Ulvaeus & Stig Anderson

27
Fields Of Gold

Words & Music by Sting

Man- y   years have passed   since those___ sum - mer days,   a -
mem - ber   me   when the___ west wind moves   up -

mong the fields___ of bar - ley.   See the chil-dren walk   as the
on   the fields___ of bar - ley.   You can tell the sun   in his

sun goes down   a - mong___   the fields___ of gold.   You'll re -
jeal - ous sky   when we   walked in fields___ of gold,

When___ we walked in fields___ of gold,   When we

walked in fields___ of gold.

58

28
Fragile

Words & Music by Sting

If blood will flow when flesh and steel are one,

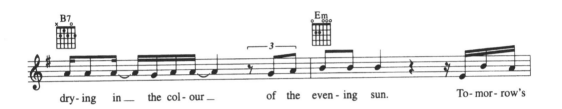

dry-ing in __ the col-our __ of the even-ing sun. To-mor-row's

rain will wash the stains a-way, __ but

some-thing in __ our minds __ will al-ways stay. __ Per-

haps this fi-nal act __ was meant __ to clinch a life-time's ar-gu-ment that

no-thing comes_ from vi - o - lence and no-thing ev - er could._ For

all those born_ be - neath_ an an - gry star, lest

we for - get___ how fra - gile we are.

On____ and on_____ the rain____ will fall_ like

tears from_ a star,_ like tears from_ a star_

on____ and on____ the rain___ will say_ how

To Coda ⊕

fra - gile _ we are, _ how fra - gile _ we are. _

60

⊕ Coda

fra - gile _ we are, _ how fra - gile _ we are, _ how

fra - gile _ we are. _

29
From A Distance

Words & Music by Julie Gold

Moderately

N.C.

From a dis-tance the world looks blue and green, and the

snow - capped moun-tains so white. From a dis-tance the oc - ean

meets the stream, and the ea - gle takes to flight. From a

F   G   Am   F   C

dis-tance there is har-mo-ny and it e-choes through the land.

G   F   C   F   C

It's the voice of hope, it's the voice of peace, it's the

F   Gsus4   G   C   G/C   F/C   G/C   C   G/C   F/C

voice of ev - 'ry - one. From a

dis- tance   we   all ___   have   e - nough, _   and   no   one   is _____   in

need.   There   are   no   guns,   no   bombs _ and   no ____   dis - ease, _   no

hun - gry   mouths ___   to   feed.   For _   a   mo- ment   we   must   be

in - stru- ments   march- ing   in   a   com- mon   band. ___   Play- ing

songs   of ___   hope, _   play- ing   songs   of ___   peace, _   they're   the   songs   of ___   ev - 'ry-

one.   God _   is   watch- ing   us,   God _   is   watch- ing   us, ___   God _   is

watch- ing   us ___   from   a   dis- tance. _

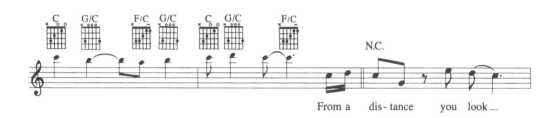

From a dis - tance you look __

like my friend, __ ev - en though __ we __ are __ at war. From a

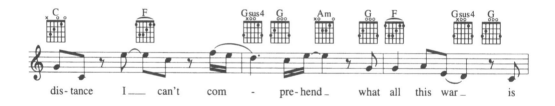

dis - tance I __ can't com - pre - hend __ what all this war __ is

for. What __ we need is love __ and har - mo - ny, __ let it

e - cho through __ the land. __ It's the hope of __ hopes, __ it's the

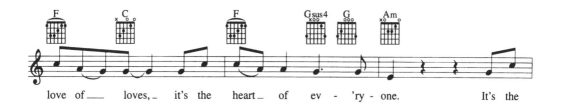

love of __ loves, _ it's the heart _ of ev - 'ry - one. It's the

hope of __ hopes, _ it's the love of __ loves, _ it's the song _ of __ ev - 'ry -

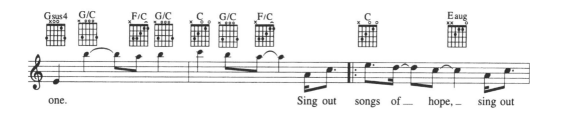

one. Sing out songs of _ hope, _ sing out

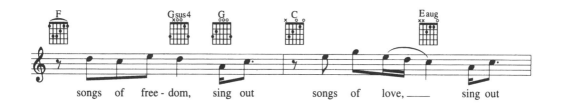

songs of free - dom, sing out songs of love, ___ sing out

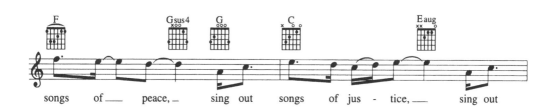

songs of __ peace, _ sing out songs of jus - tice, ___ sing out

Repeat to fade

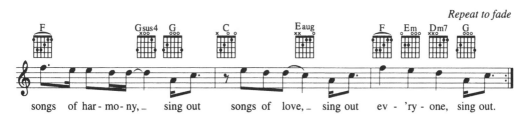

songs of har - mo- ny, _ sing out songs of love, _ sing out ev - 'ry - one, sing out.

30
The Girl From Ipanema (Garota De Ipanema)

Words by Vinicius De Moraes
Music by Antonio Carlos Jobim

sad - ly. _____ How _____ can I tell her I

love her? _____ Yes, _____ I would give my heart

glad - ly, _____ But each day when she walks to the sea, she

looks straight a - head not at me. Tall and tan and young_

_ and love - ly, the girl _ from I - pa - ne - ma goes walk - ing, and when_

she pass - es I smile, _ but she does - n't see,

She just does - n't see, No, she does - n't

1. see. 2. see. _____

31
Funny How Time Slips Away

Words & Music by Willie Nelson

32
Good People

Words & Music by Jack Johnson

to tell me how great it's all gon-na be.

You might no -tice some he-si-ta-tion. What's im-por-tant to you is not im-por-tant to me.

Oh, way down by the edge of your rea-sons, well, it's be-gin-ning to show, and

Coda

D.S. al Coda

all I real-ly wan-na know is: Where'd all the good peo-ple

They got this and that, and a rat-tle a tat, test - ing one, two, now what you gon-na do? Bad news, mis-used, gim-me some truth, you got too much to lose. Who's side are we on? Ev-'ry day, ev-'ry way, O.-K., what e-ver you say. Run the re-so-lute but in the mood to o - bey.

Sta-tion to sta-tion, de-sen - si - ti-zing the na-tion. Go-ing, go - ing, gone.

33

Goodbye Yellow Brick Road

Words & Music by Elton John & Bernie Taupin

1. When are you gon-na come down, when are you going to land?
2. What do you think you'll do then? I bet they shoot down your plane.

I should have stayed on the farm, should have list-
It'll take you a cou-ple of vod-ka and ton-ics to

- ened to my old man. You know you can't hold me for-ev-
get you on your feet a-gain. May-be you'll get a re-place

- er, I did-n't sign up with you. I'm
- ment, there's plen-ty like me to be found.

not a pre-sent for your friends to o-pen, this boy's too young to be
Mon-grels who ain't got a pen-ny, sing-ing for tid-bits like

sing-ing the blues.
you on the ground.

Ah._____   Ah._____   So

good - bye_ yel - low brick   road,_____ where the dogs of so - ci - et - y howl.

_   You can't plant me in your pent -   house,_____ I'm go - ing back_ to my

plough.   Back to   the howl - ing old owl__ in the woods,_   hunt - ing the hor - ny back

toad.   Oh, I've fin - 'ly de - cid - ed my   fu - ture lies   be-

yond   the yel - low brick   road._____   Ah._____

1.   **2.**

____   Ah._____   Ah.   Ah.

73

34
Guantanamera

Words adapted by Julian Orbon from a poem by José Marti
Music by Julian Orbon & Pete Seeger

Guan-ta-na-me-ra   gua-ji - ra Guan-ta-na-me-ra

Guan-ta-na-me - ra   gua-ji-ra Guan-ta-na-me - ra!   ra!

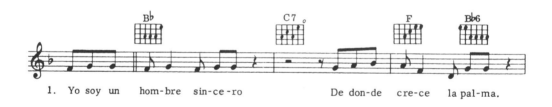

1. Yo soy un hom-bre sin-ce-ro   De don-de cre-ce la pal-ma.

Yo soy un   hom-bre sin-ce-ro   De don-de cre - ce la

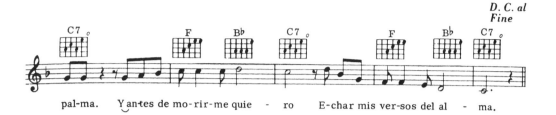

pal-ma.   Y an-tes de mo-rir-me quie - ro   E-char mis ver-sos del al - ma.

2. Mi verso es de un verde claro,
    Y de un carmin encendido.
    Mi verso es de un verde claro,
    Y de un carmin encendido.
    Mi verso es un cierro herido
    Que busca en el monte amparo.
        [Chorus]

3. Con los pobres de la tierra
    Quiero yo mi suerte echar.
    Con los pobres de la tierra
    Quiero yo mi suerte echar.
    El arroyo de la sierra
    Me complace mas que el mar.
        [Chorus]

Literal translation:

1. I am a truthful man from the land
    of palm trees.
    Before dying I want to share these
    poems of my soul.

2. My poems are light green,
    but they are also flaming crimson.
    My verses are like a wounded faun
    seeking refuge in the forest.

3. With the poor people of this earth
    I want to share my fate.
    The little streams of the mountains
    please me more than the sea.

35
Hey Jude

Words & Music by John Lennon & Paul McCartney

who plays ___ it cool ___ By mak - ing his world ___ a lit - tle cold-
___ Hey Jude, ___ you'll do. ___ The move - ment you need ___ is on ___ your shoul-

- er.___ Da da da da ___ da da da da   da   Hey   Hey ___
- der.___

Jude, _____ don't make it   bad;   take a   sad song___ and make it

bet - ter.___   Re - mem - ber to let her un - der your   skin   then you'll be - gin___

___ to make it   bet - ter, bet-ter, bet-ter, bet-ter,   bet-ter, bet-ter, Oh _____

yeh yeh yeh yeh yeh yeh yeh   da da da da   da da da da   Hey___ Jude.

repeat and fade

da   da   da   da da da da   da da da da   Hey___ Jude.

77

36
Hallelujah

Words & Music by Leonard Cohen

1. Well, I heard there was a se - cret chord that Da - vid played and it
(2.) faith was strong but you need - ed proof. You saw her bath - ing
(3, 4. *See block lyrics*)

pleased the Lord, but you don't real - ly care for mu - sic, do ya?
on the roof, her beau - ty and the moon - light ov - er - threw ya.

Well, it goes like this: the fourth, the fifth, the mi - nor fall and the
And she tied you to her kitch - en chair and she broke your throne and she

ma - jor lift, the baf - fled king com - pos - ing Hal - le - lu - jah._
cut your hair, and from your lips you drew the Hal - le - lu - jah._

Hal - le - lu - jah.   Hal - le - lu - jah.   Hal - le - lu - jah.   Hal - le -

1, 2, 3.

- lu - - jah.   2. Well, your -jah.

Verse 1
Well, baby, I've been here before,
I've seen this room, and I've walked this floor,
You know, I used to live alone before I knew you.
And I've seen your flag on the marble arch,
And love is not a victory march,
It's a cold and it's a broken Hallelujah.

Verse 2
Well, there was a time when you let me know
What's really going on below,
But now you never show that to me, do ya?
But remember when I moved in you
And the holy dove was moving too,
And every breath we drew was Hallelujah?

37
Grace

Words & Music by Jeff Buckley & Gary Lucas

1. There's the
2. And she
3. And I

moon   ask - ing to   stay   long   e - nough   for   the
weeps   on   my   arm,   so ea   -   -   sy   to
feel   them   drown my   name,   walk - ing   to   the

clouds_   to fly_   me a - way._____   Oh, it's my   time com - ing,_
bright   lights   in   sor - row.   Oh,   drink a bit of wine, we
know   and   forget with this kiss.   I'm not   a - fraid to

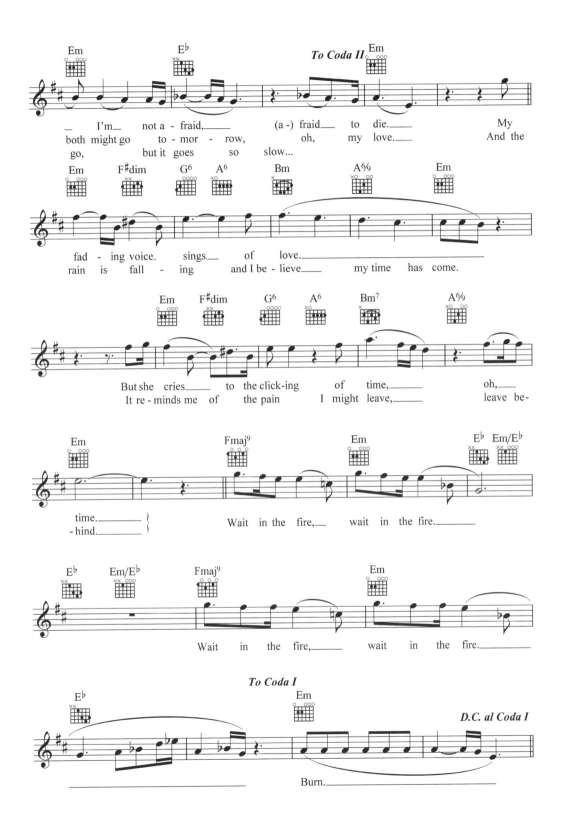

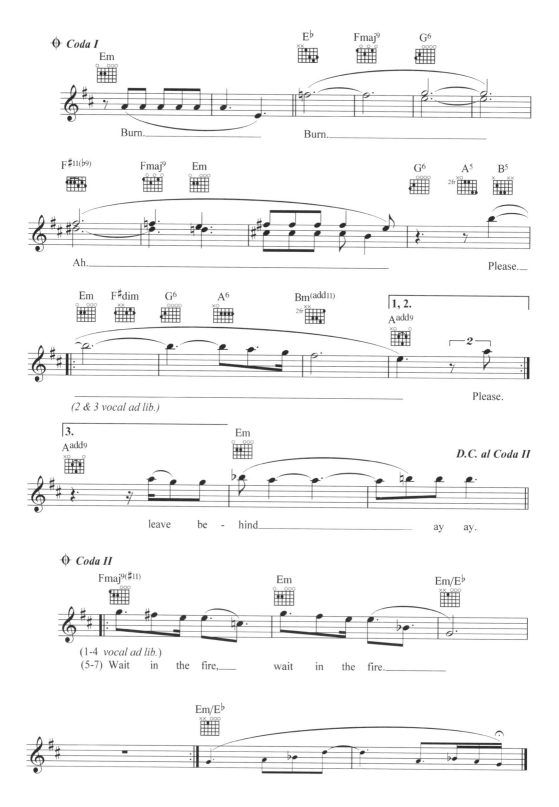

38
Here, There And Everywhere

Words & Music by John Lennon & Paul McCartney

39
Homeward Bound

Words & Music by Paul Simon

Lyrically

I'm sit - tin' in the rail - way sta - tion got a tick - et for my des - ti - na - tion. ___

Mm. ___

On a tour of one night stands my suit - case and gui - tar in hand, And ev - 'ry stop is neat - ly planned for a po - et and a one man band. ___

40
How Deep Is Your Love

Words & Music by Barry Gibb, Maurice Gibb & Robin Gibb

ly leave.—}
ly do.—} And it's me you need_ to show: ____ how deep is your love. How deep_

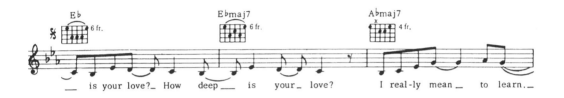

_ is your love?_ How deep___ is your_ love? I real-ly mean _ to learn._

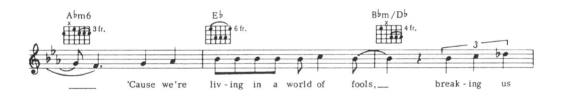

_____ 'Cause we're liv-ing in a world of fools,_ break-ing us

down when they all ____ should let us be. ____ We be-long_

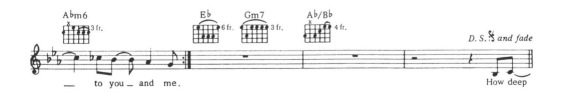

_ to you _ and me. How deep

D. S. and fade

41
Hurt

Words & Music by Trent Reznor

1. I hurt my - self___ to - day to
2. I wear this crown___ of thorns up -

see if I___ still feel. I fo - cused on the pain,___
-on my li - ars chair. Full of bro - ken thoughts,___

___ the on - ly thing___ that's real. The
___ I can - not___ re - pair. Be -

nee - dle tears a hole,___ the old fa - mil - iar sting.___ Try to
-neath the stains of time___ the feel - ings dis - ap - pear.___

kill it all a - way___ but I re - mem - ber ev - 'ry - thing.___
You are some-one else,___ I am still right here.___

Am⁷   Fadd9   C   G

What have I___ be - come____ my sweet-est friend?_

Am⁷   Fadd9   C   G

Ev -'ry - one___ I know___ goes a - way___ in the end.___ And

Am⁷   Fadd9   G

you could have__ it all,___ my em - pire of dirt.

1.

Am⁷   Fadd9   G

I will let___ you down,___ I will make_ you hurt._

Am   C   D   Am   C   Dsus²

2.

G   Am⁷

I will make_ you hurt. If I could start__ a - gain,_

Fadd9   G

_ a mil - lion miles__ a - way,___

Am⁷   Fadd9   G

I would keep_ my - self,___ I would find__ a way.

42
I Don't Want To Talk About It

Words & Music by Danny Whitten

1. I can tell by your eyes_ that you've prob-'ly been cry-ing for-
stand all a-lone,_ will the sha-dow hide the col-ours of my

(%Instrumental to fade)

-ev - er.___ And the stars in the sky_ don't mean
heart; blue for the tears, black for the night's fears. The

no - thing to you, they're a mir - ror.___

I don't wan -na talk a-bout_ it, how you broke my heart.___

If I stay just a lit-tle bit long-er, if I stay, won't you lis-ten_ to my

heart,_____ whoa,_ my_ heart? 2. If I heart?

43
I Walk The Line

Words & Music by Johnny Cash

1. I keep a close watch on this heart of mine.
2. I find it ve - ry, ve - ry ea - sy to be true.
3. As sure as night is dark and day is light.

(Verses 4 & 5 see additional lyrics)

I keep my eyes wide op - en all the time.
I find my - self a - lone when each day is through.
I keep you on my mind both day and night.

I keep the ends out for the tie that binds,
Yes I'll ad - mit that I'm a fool for you,
And hap - pi - ness I've known proves that it's right,

Play 5 times

be - cause you're mine, I walk the line.

Verse 4
You've got a way to keep me on your side.
You give me cause for love that I can't hide.
For you I know I'd even try to turn the tide,
Because you're mine, I walk the line.

Verse 5
As Verse 1

44
Imagine

Words & Music by John Lennon

♩=70

I-ma-gine there's no heav - en,   It's ea-sy if you

try, _____   No hell _ be-low _____ us,

A-bove us on-ly sky.   I - ma-gine all   the peo -

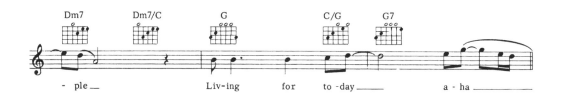

- ple _   Liv-ing   for to -day _____   a - ha _____

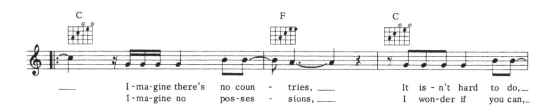

I-ma-gine there's no coun - tries, _   It is - n't hard to do,
I-ma-gine no pos-ses - sions, _   I won-der if you can,

No-thing to kill __ or die _____ for,
No need for greed __ or hun - ger,

And no re - lig-ion too. _____ I - ma-gine all the peo -
A broth-er - hood of man. _____ I - ma-gine all the peo -

- ple __ Liv-ing life in peace __ yu-huh _____
- ple __ Shar-ing all the world __ yu-huh _____

__ { You may say _____ I'm a drea-mer, But I'm not __ the on-ly one. __

__ I hope some day _____ you'll join us, __

And the world ___ will be one. _____ live as one. __

45
In The Summertime

Words & Music by Ray Dorset

Moderately fast

mf
(Instrumental)

1. In the

Sum - mer - time when the wea - ther is high,___ You can
(Verses 2, 3 & 4, see block lyrics)

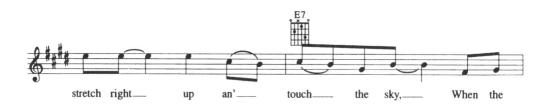

stretch right___ up an'___ touch___ the sky,___ When the

wea - ther's___ fine, you got wo - men, you got wo - men on your

mind.   *(Instrumental)*   Have   a

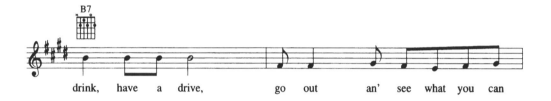

drink,   have   a   drive,   go   out   an' see what you can

Fine

find.   *(Instrumental)*   2. If   her
                                                              3. We're not
                                                              4. When the

2. If her daddy's rich
   Take her out for a meal,
   If her daddy's poor
   Just do as you feel,
   Speed along the lane,
   Do a ton, or a ton an' twenty five,
   When the sun goes down
   You can make it, make it good in a lay-by.

3. We're not grey people,
   We're not dirty, we're not mean,
   We love everybody
   But we do as we please,
   When the weather's fine
   We go fishing or go swimming in the sea,
   We're always happy,
   Life's for living, yeah! That's our philosophy.

4. When the winter's here,
   Yeah! It's party time,
   Bring a bottle, wear your bright clothes,
   It'll soon be summertime,
   And we'll sing again,
   We'll go driving, or maybe we'll settle down,
   If she's rich, if she's nice,
   Bring your friends, an' we'll all go into town.
   (al Fine)

46
Jolene

Words & Music by Dolly Parton

talks a-bout ___ you in his sleep ___ and there's no-thing I ___ can

do to keep ___ from cry - ing when he calls your name Jo - lene. ___

And I can eas - 'ly

un - der - stand ___ how you could eas - 'ly take my man, ___ but you

don't know what he means to me Jo - lene. ___

D.S. al Coda
(with repeat)

⊕ *CODA*

Jo- can. ___

Jo - lene ___

Jo - lene. ___

47
If You Could Read My Mind

Words & Music by Gordon Lightfoot

48
Knockin' On Heaven's Door

Words & Music by Bob Dylan

49
Let There Be Love

Words & Music by Noel Gallagher

B♭9/F

let__ there be__ love.____

Am Fmaj7

Am

Come on____ ba - by blue,____ shake up your

E7/G#

G5

ti - red eyes,____ the world is wait - ing for__ you.____ May all____

D/F#

Fmaj7

___ your dream - ing fill____ the emp - ty____ sky.____

D7/F#

G5 E7 Am

But if it makes you__ hap - py,

C E7

keep on____ clap - ping, just re - mem - ber I'll__ be by__ your__

Am Am7/G Fmaj7

side.____ And if you don't let go,____ it's

101

50
Life For Rent

Words & Music by Dido Armstrong & Rollo Armstrong

that if my life_____ is___ for___ rent, and I

don't learn to buy,____ well, I de - serve____ no - thing more than I____

1.
____ get 'cause no - thing I_____ have_____ is tru - ly mine.____

2. I

2, 3.
____ And if my____ life_____ is____ for___ rent and I____

____ don't___ learn to buy,_____ well, I de - serve____ no - thing more_ than I___

To Coda ⊕
____ get 'cause no - thing I_____ have_____ is tru - ly mine.____ while my__

____ heart is a shield and I won't let it down__

104

while I am so a - fraid to fail,

so I won't ev - en try.

Well how can I say I'm a - live.

D.S. al Coda

Well if my

Coda

'cause no - thing I

have is tru - ly mine, 'cause no - thing I

have is tru - ly mine, 'cause no - thing I

have is tru - ly mine.

51
Light My Fire

Words & Music by Jim Morrison, Robbie Krieger, Ray Manzarek & John Densmore

52
Lost Cause

Words & Music by Beck Hansen

1. They're sor-ry   eyes,___   that cut through_ bone.___
2. There's too ma-ny peo-ple,   you used to___ know.___

That make it   hard,___   to leave you a-lone.___
They see you   com-ing,   they see you   go.___

Leave you   here___   wear-ing your robes.___
They know your   sec-rets,   and you know theirs.___

Wav-ing your   guns,___   at some bo-dy new.___
This town is   cra - zy,   no-bo-dy cares.___

Ba-by you're a   lost,___   ba-by you're a   lost,___

ba-by you're a   lost___   cause.

1.

2.

I'm tir-ed of fight - ing,   I'm tir-ed of fight - ing.

53
Love And Affection

Words & Music by Joan Armatrading

Make love, oh,___
(Lov-er ooh hoo.)

___ with af - fec - tion. Sing me a - no -ther love song but this

time with a lit-tle de-di-ca-tion. Sing it, sing it. (Sing it, sing it.) You know that's what I like.

1.
(Lov -er ooh hoo.) Once more with the feel -ing.

2.
With af -fec - tion.

Ooh ooh with a lit -tle de - di - ca -tion. (Lov - er ooh hoo.)

Once more with the feel -ing. Ooh ooh. You know that's what I like.

(Lov - er ooh hoo.) Ooh hoo.___

54
Love Is All Around

Words & Music by Reg Presley

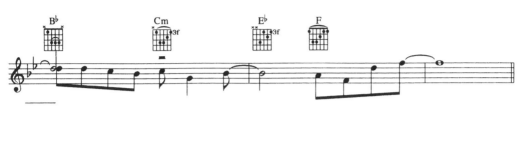

You know I love you, I al- ways— will,— My mind's made up by the

way that I feel,— There's no be - gin - ning, There'll be no— end,— 'Cause

on my— love— you can de - pend.———

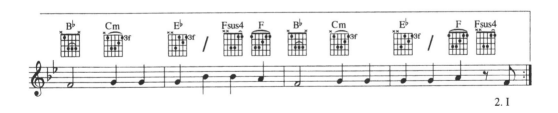

2. I

Got to keep it mov - ing. It's

55
The Long And
Winding Road

Words & Music by John Lennon & Paul McCartney

The long and win-ding road that __ leads to your door
wild and win-dy night that the rain washed a - way

will nev-er dis-ap - pear, I've seen that road be - fore.
has left a pool of tears cry-ing for the day.

It al-ways leads me here, lead me to your_ door. The
Why leave me stand-ing here, let me know the __

way. Man-y times I've been a-lone, and man-y times I've cried,

An-y-way, you'll nev-er know the man-y ways I've tried, But still they lead me

back to the long win-ding road. You left me stand-ing

here a long, long time a - go, Don't leave me

wait-ing here, lead me to your_ door.

56
Love Me Tender

Words & Music by Elvis Presley & Vera Matson

Moderately slow

1. Love me ten-der, love me sweet; Nev-er let me go.
2. Love me ten-der, love me long; Take me to your heart.
3. Love me ten-der, love me dear; Tell me you are mine.

[opt.] When at last my dreams come true, Dar-ling, this I know:

You have made my life com-plete, And I love you so.
For it's there that I be-long, And we'll nev-er part.
I'll be yours through all the years Till the end of time.

Hap-pi-ness will fol-low you Eve-ry-where you go.

Chorus

Love me ten-der, love me true; All my dreams ful-

fill. For, my dar-lin', I love you,

1,2

And I al-ways will.

3 (and opt.)

And I al-ways will.

57
Love Minus Zero/No Limit

Words & Music by Bob Dylan

1. My love,___ she speaks like si - lence,
2. Peo-ple car - ry ro - ses,
(3.) dime stores and bus sta - tions,

(Verses 4-9 see block lyrics)

with - out i - deals or vio - lence.
make pro - mi-ses_ by the hou - rs.
peo - ple talk of si - tu - a - tions,

She does-n't have to say she's faith - ful, yet she's true,___
My love, she laughs like the flow - ers; Val - en - tines___
read books, re - peat quo - ta - tions, draw con - clu -

___ like ice,___ like fire.___
can't buy her.___
- sions on___ the wall.

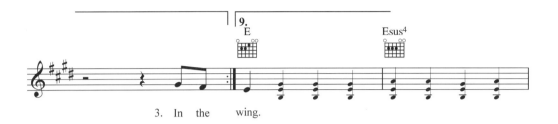

3. In   the   wing.

Verse 4
Some speak of the future;
My love, she speaks softly.
She knows there's no success like failure,
And that failure's no success at all.

Verse 5
The cloak and dagger dangles,
Madams light the candles,
In ceremonies of the horsemen,
Even the pawn must hold a grudge.

Verse 6
Statues made of matchsticks
Crumble into one another.
My love winks, she does not bother;
She knows too much to argue or to judge.

Verse 7
Instrumental.

Verse 8
The bridge at midnight trembles,
The country doctor rambles,
Bankers' nieces seek perfection,
Expecting all the gifts wise men bring.

Verse 9
The wind howls like a hammer,
The night blows rainy,
My love, she's like some raven
At my window with a broken wing.

58
Lover, You Should've Come Over

Words & Music by Jeff Buckley

Slow and free

1. Look - ing out the door, I see the rain fall up - on the fu - neral
(2.) bro - ken down and hun - gry for your love with no way to

(Verse 3 see block lyric)

___ mourn - ers. Pa - rad - ing in a wake of sad re -
feed it. Where are you to

- la - tions as their shoes fill up with wa - ter.___
night, child, you know how much I need it?

1.

May - be I'm too young to keep good love from go - ing wrong. But to-

To Coda

- night you're___ on___ my mind, so___ you'll nev - er know. 2. I'm

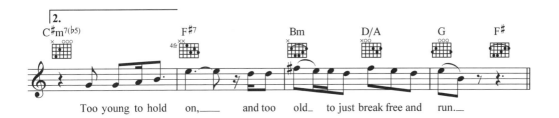

Too young to hold on,___ and too old_ to just break free and run.__

Some-times a man gets car-ried a-way when he feels like he should be_ hav-ing his

fun. And much too blind to see(the) da-mage he's done.__ And some-times a man must a-

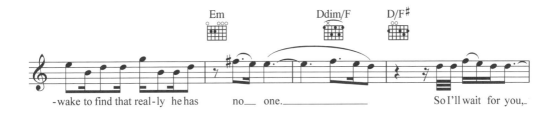

-wake to find that real-ly he has no__ one._____ So I'll wait for you,_

__ and I'll burn. Will I ev-er see your_ sweet re-turn?_

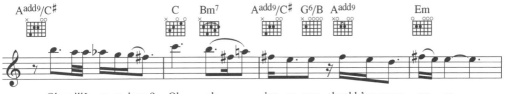

Oh, will I ev-er learn?_ Oh, oh,____ lov-er, you should-'ve come ov-er,____

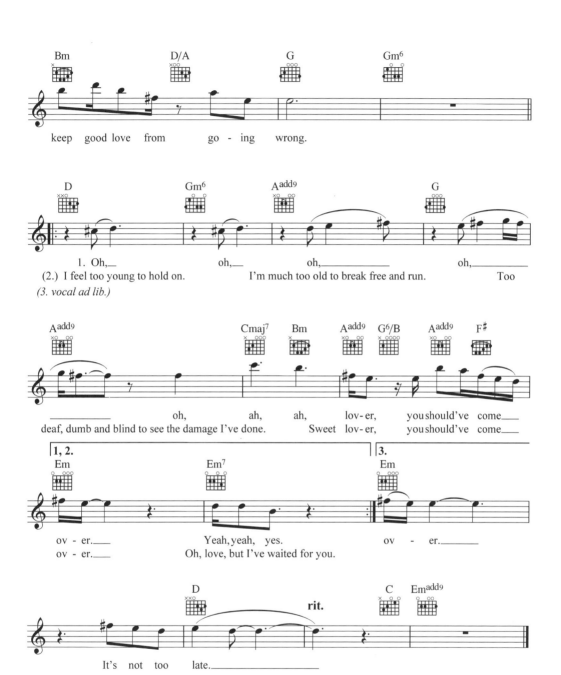

Bm   **D/A**   **G**   **Gm⁶**

keep   good   love   from   go - ing   wrong.

D   **Gm⁶**   **A^add9**   **G**

     1. Oh,__   oh,__   oh,_____   oh,_____
(2.) I feel too young to hold on.   I'm much too old to break free and run.   Too
(3. vocal ad lib.)

A^add9   **Cmaj⁷**   **Bm**   **A^add9**   **G⁶/B**   **A^add9**   **F♯**

_____   oh,   ah,   ah,   lov- er,   you should've come__
deaf, dumb and blind to see the damage I've done.   Sweet lov- er,   you should've come__

1, 2.			**3.**

Em   **Em⁷**   **Em**

ov - er.__   Yeah, yeah,   yes.   ov - er._____
ov - er.__   Oh, love, but I've waited for you.

D   **rit.**   **C**   **Em^add9**

It's   not   too   late._____

Verse 3:
Lonely is the room, the bed is made,
The open window lets the rain in.
Burning in the corner is the only one,
Who dreams he had you with him.

59
(Marie's The Name)
His Latest Flame

Words & Music by Doc Pomus & Mort Shuman

He was gone but still his words kept re-turn-in'.

What else was there for me to do but cry?

Would you be - lieve

that yes - ter - day, this girl was in my arms and

swore to me she'd be mine e - ter - nal - ly? And Ma-rie's the

1.

name of his lat - est flame.

2. *Repeat to fade*

flame.

125

60
Maggie May

Words & Music by Rod Stewart & Martin Quittenton

stole my heart___ and that's___ what real-ly hurts.___
stole my soul___ and that's a pain I can do___ with-out.___
stole my heart___ I could-n't leave you if___ I tried.___

2.The

I sup-pose___ I could col-lect my books and get on back to school___

or steal my dad-dy's cue___ and make a liv-ing out of play-ing pool.___

Or find my-self a rock 'n' roll band that needs___ a help-ing hand.___

— Oh, Mag-gie I wish I'd nev-er seen your face._____

You made a first class fool out of me but I'm as blind as a fool can be.___

— You stole my heart___ but I love you an-y-way.___

127

61
Me And Julio Down By The Schoolyard

Words & Music by Paul Simon

Moderately bright

The ma-ma pa-ja-ma rolled out of bed, and she ran to the po-lice

sta-tion. When the pa-pa found out, he be-gan to shout,—and he

start-ed the in-ves-ti-ga-tion. It's a-gainst the law, (tacet - - -)

It was a-gainst the law. what the ma-ma saw,

It was a-gainst the law.— The ma-ma looked down and
(In a) cou-ple of days they come and

spit on the ground ev-'ry time my name—gets men-tioned. The
take me a-way, but the press let the sto-ry leak. And when the

pa-pa said "Oy, if I get that boy — I'm gon-na stick him in the house of de-ten-
rad- i - cal priest come to get me re-leased ___ we's all on the cov-er of News

(tacet - - - -)

- tion".
- week.

Well, I'm on my way, ___ I don't know

where I'm go in', ___ I'm on my way, ___ I'm tak-in' my time

___ but I don't know where. ___ Good-bye Ro - sie, the Queen of Co-ro-

- na, See you, me and Ju - lio down by the School -yard.

See you, me and Ju - lio down by the School-yard.

In a See you,

me and Ju - lio down by the School - yard. ___

129

62
Michelle

Words & Music by John Lennon & Paul McCartney

63
More Than Words

Words & Music by Nuno Bettencourt & Gary Cherone

Verse 2:
Now I've tried to talk to you
And make you understand
All you have to do is close your eyes
And just reach out your hands
And touch me
Hold me close don't ever let me go
More than words
Is all I ever needed you to show
Then you wouldn't have to say
That you love me
'Cause I'd already know.

What would you do *etc.*

133

64
Mrs. Robinson

Words & Music by Paul Simon

Fine

We'd

VERSE

G7

like   to   know a   lit — tle   bit   a — bout   you   for   our

C7

files, _____   We'd   like   to   help   you

learn   to   help   your — self. _____

F7   Bb   Eb

Look a — round you,   all   you   see   are   sym — pa — thet — ic

Cm   G

eyes. _____   Stroll   a —

F   *D.S. al Fine*

— round   the   grounds   un — til   you   feel   at   home, and   here's   to

135

65
Mad World

Words & Music by Roland Orzabal

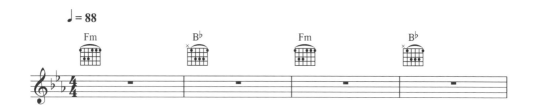

1. All a-round me are fa-mi-liar fa-ces, worn out pla-ces,
2. Chil-dren wait-ing for the day they feel good, hap-py birth-day,

worn out fa-ces. Bright and ear-ly for their dai-ly ra-ces,
hap-py birth-day. And I feel the way that ev-'ry child should

go-ing no-where, go-ing no-where. Their tears are fill-ing
sit and lis-ten, sit and lis-ten. Went to school and I was

up their glass-es, no ex-pres-sion, no ex-pres-sion.
ve-ry ner-vous, no-one knew me, no-one knew me.

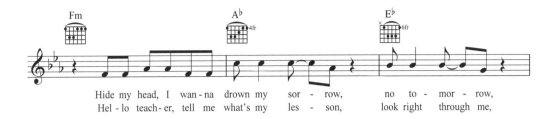

Fm

Hide my head, I wan-na drown my sor - row, no to - mor - row,
Hel -lo teach-er, tell me what's my les - son, look right through me,

A♭

E♭

B♭

Fm

B♭

no to - mor - row._____
look right through me._____ } And I find it kin-da fun-ny, I find it kin-da

Fm

B♭

Fm

sad that dreams in which I'm dy-ing are the best I've ev-er had. I find it hard to

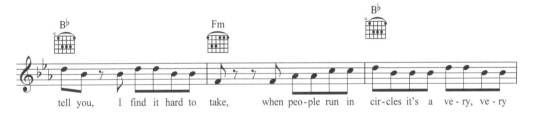

B♭

Fm

B♭

tell you, I find it hard to take, when peo-ple run in cir-cles it's a ve-ry, ve-ry

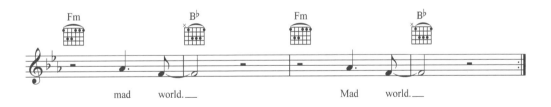

Fm

B♭

Fm

B♭

mad world.____ Mad world.____

Fm

B♭

Fm

B♭

En-larg -en your__ world. Mad world.____

66
Mr. Tambourine Man

Words & Music by Bob Dylan

Moderate 2

Hey! Mis-ter Tam-bou-rine Man, play a song for me, I'm not sleep-y and there is no place I'm go-in' to.

Hey! Mis-ter Tam-bou-rine Man, play a song for me. In the jin-gle jan-gle morn-in' I'll come fol - low-in' you.

fine

Verse

Tho' I know that eve-nin's em -pire has re - turned in - to sand, Van -ished from my hand, Left me blind-ly here to stand, but still not sleep-in'. My wea-ri - ness a - maz - es me, I'm brand - ed on my feet. I have no one to meet, And the an - cient emp -ty street's too dead for dream-in'.

67
No Regrets

Words & Music by Tom Rush

68
No Woman, No Cry

Words & Music by Vincent Ford

when we used — to sit   in the gov-ern-ment yard in

Trench-town.   { 1. O - ba, O - b - serv - ing the
                        2.3. And then Geor-gie would make a

hyp - o - crites   as they would   min - gle with the good peo - ple we
fi - re - light   as it was   log wood burn - in' through the

meet,   good friends _ we had _____ oh
night.   Then we __ would cook _____ corn

good friends we've lost _   a- long the way. ___
meal por - ridge   of which I'll share with you. ___

In _ this bright _ fu - ture   you _ can't for - get your _ past
My feet _ is my   on - ly _ car - riage, _

141

so, dry your tears ___ I ___ say. And
so, I've got to push on ___ through, but while I'm gone I mean...

Ev-'ry-thing's gon-na be al-right. Ev-'ry-thing's gon-na be al-right.

1.
Ev-'ry-thing's gon-na be al-right. Ev-'ry-thing's gon-na be al-right.

2.
Ev-'ry-thing's gon-na be al-right so, wom-an, no cry.

No, no wom-an, no wom-an, no cry. ___

___ Oh, my lit-tle sis-ter don't shed no tears. ___

No wom-an, no cry. ___ *Guitar solo ad lib.*

143

69
Norwegian Wood

Words & Music by John Lennon & Paul McCartney

Slowly

I once had a girl, or should I say she once had me;

She showed me her room, is-n't it good Nor-we-gian wood. She

asked me to stay and she told me to sit an - y - where, So
told me she worked in the morn-ing and start-ed to laugh. I

I looked a-round and I no-ticed there was-n't a chair.
told her I did-n't and crawled off to sleep in the bath.

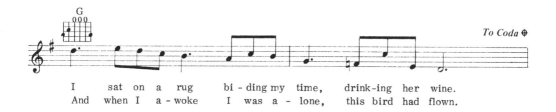

I   sat on a   rug   bi - ding my time,   drink-ing her wine.
And   when I a - woke   I was a - lone,   this bird had flown.

We   talked un-til two   and then she said   "It's time for bed."
So   I   lit a fire,   Is - n't it good   Nor-we - gian wood.

D.%. al Coda

She

⊕ *CODA*

145

70
Northern Sky

Words & Music by Nick Drake

Tuning: D A D G D G or C G C F C F
Capo: 1st Fret   Capo: 3rd Fret

1, 4. I ne-ver felt ma-gic cra-
2. I've been a long time and I'm
3.   Would you love me for my

- zy as this,   I ne-ver saw moons knew the mean-ing of the sea.
wait-ing,   been a long time that I've blown.
mon- ey?   Would you love me for my head?

I ne-ver held e-mo-tion in the   palm of my hand   or felt sweet   bree-zes in the
I've been a long   time that I've   wan dered   through the   peo-ple I have
Would you love me through the   win - ter?   Would you   love me till I'm

top of a tree._ But now you're here,   bright- en   my north - ern   sky._____
known.   Oh,_   if   you would and you could   straight en   my new mind's eye._____
dead?   Oh,_   if   you would and you could   come blow your horn   on   high._____

tacet on repeat - - - - - - - - -|

Fig. 2 - - - - - - - - - - -|

71
Not Fade Away

Words & Music by Charles Hardin & Norman Petty

Brightly

I'm gon-na tell you how it's gon-na be,____
My love is big-ger than a Cad-il-lac,____

You're gon-na give-a your love to me.____
I try to show it and you drive me back.____

I wan-na love you night and day; ____ You
Your love for me has got to be real; ____ For

know my love ____ not ____ fade a-way,____ Well, you
you to know____ just ____ how I feel,____ A

know my love ___ not ___ fade a-way.____
love for real ___ not ___ fade a-way.____

Repeat then
D.S to fine.
Fine

72

Other Side Of The World

Words & Music by KT Tunstall & Martin Terefe

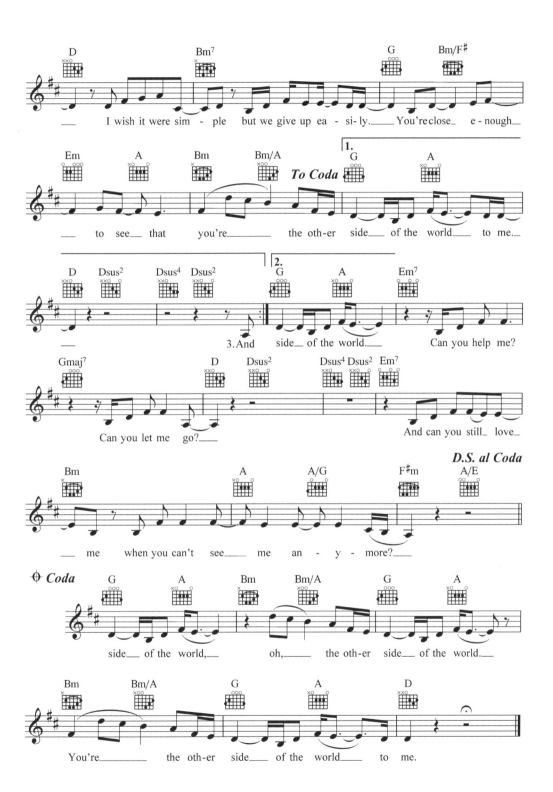

I wish it were sim - ple but we give up ea - si- ly.__ You're close__ e - nough__ to see__ that you're__ the oth-er side__ of the world__ to me.__

To Coda

3.And side__ of the world.__ Can you help me?

Can you let me go?__ And can you still__ love__

D.S. al Coda

__ me when you can't see__ me an - y - more?__

Coda

side__ of the world,__ oh,__ the oth-er side__ of the world.__

You're__ the oth-er side__ of the world__ to me.

73
One Day I'll Fly Away

Words by Will Jennings
Music by Joe Sample

Lyrics:

through with me. Why live life from

dream to dream and dread the day that dreaming ends.

One day I'll fly a - way,

74
Patience Of Angels

Words & Music by Boo Hewerdine

try ___ the pa-tience of an - gels, ___

an - gels. ___ (2.) And you

There's a door ___ in a wall ___ in a house ___ in a

street, ___ in a town ___ where ___ no-one knows ___ her name, ___

she's the pa-tience of an - gels.

Does she

know, ___ I don't know, ___ but from here ___ I can

153

2. And you know something's wrong
   When the morning hurts your eyes.
   And the baby won't stop crying,
   You'll be waiting till you die.
   Would I be any good,
   And if I was would I find
   That it would try...

154

75
Pink Moon

Words & Music by Nick Drake

Tuning: D A D G D F♯ *or* C G C F C E
Capo: 2nd Fret

76
Romeo And Juliet

Words & Music by Mark Knopfler

♩ = 96

1 A love struck Ro-me-o sings a street-suss se-re-nade,— lay-ing ev'ry-bo-dy low
(Verses 2 & 3, see block lyrics)

with a love song that he made, finds— a street-light, steps out of the shade, says some-thing like,

"You and me babe,— how a-bout it?"— Ju-li-et says, "Hey, it's Ro-me-o,

you near-ly gim-me a heart at-tack" He's un-der-neath the win-dow, she's sing-ing

"Hey la, my boy-friend's back, you should-n't come a-round here, sing-ing up at peo-ple like that,"

An-y-way, what you gon-na do a-bout— it? Ju-li-

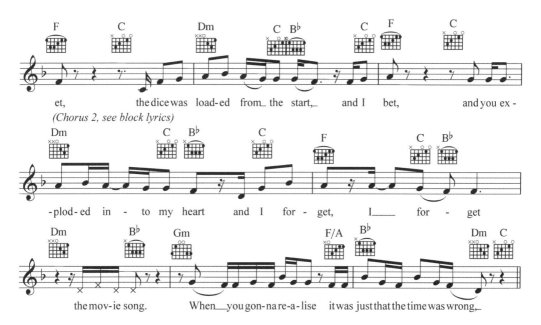

et,   the dice was load-ed from the start,_ and I bet,   and you ex -

(Chorus 2, see block lyrics)

-plod-ed in - to my heart   and I for - get,   I_   for - get

the mov-ie song.   When_you gon-na re-a-lise   it was just that the time was wrong,_

(Play three times)

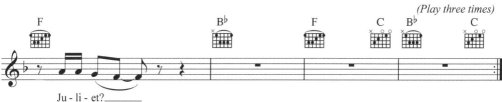

Ju - li - et?_____

Verse 2:
Come up on different streets,
They both were streets of shame.
Both dirty, both mean,
Yes, and the dream was just the same.
And I dreamed your dream for you,
And now your dream is real,
How can you look at me as if I was
Just another one of your deals?

Where you can fall for chains of silver
You can fall for chains of gold,
You can fall for pretty strangers
And the promises they hold.
You promised me everything,
You promised me thick and thin, yeah.
Now you just say "Oh Romeo, yeah,
You know I used to have a scene with him".

Chorus 2:
Juliet, when we made love you used to cry,
You said, "I love you like the stars above,
I'll love you till I die."
There's a place for us, you know the movie song,
When you gonna realise
It was just that the time was wrong, Juliet?

Verse 3:
I can't do the talks
Like they talk on the T.V.
And I can't do a love song
Like the way it's meant to be,
I can't do everything
But I'd do anything for you,
I can't do anything
Except be in love with you.

And all I do is miss you
And the way we used to be,
All do is keep the beat
And bad company,
All I do is kiss you
Through the bars of a rhyme,
Julie, I'd do the stars with you
Any time.

(Chorus 3 as Chorus 2)

157

77
Nothing Ever Happens

Words & Music by Justin Currie

Moderately

Post of - fice clerks put up signs say - ing po - si - tion
(Verses 2, 3 & 4, see block lyrics)
closed,_____ And sec - re - t'ries turn off type -

writ - ers and put on their coats._____

Ja - ni - tors pad - lock the gates for se - cu - ri - ty

guards to pa - trol, And ba - che - lors phone up their

friends for a drink, while the mar - ried ones turn on a chat show.

1.
And they'll all be lone - ly to - night, and

lone - ly to - mor - row. And no - thing

ev - er hap - pens, No - thing hap - pens at all.

The need - le re - turns to the start of the song and we

all sing a - long like be - fore. And we'll all be

lone - ly to - night, and lone - ly to - mor - row.

D.C. al Coda

4. And

159

Coda

And no-thing ev - er hap-pens, No-thing hap-pens at all. They'll burn down the Sy - na-gogues at six o' - clock, And we'll all go a - long like be - fore. And we'll all be lone - ly to - night and lone - ly to - mor - row.

2. Gentlemen time please, you know we can't serve anymore
   Now the traffic lights change to stop when there's nothing to go
   And by five o'clock everything's dead
   And every third car is a cab
   And ignorant people sleep in their beds
   Like the doped white mice in the college lab.

3. Telephone exchanges click while there's nobody there
   The Martians could land in the car park and no one would care
   Closed-circuit cameras in department stores
   Shoot the same movie every day
   And the stars of these films neither die nor get killed
   Just survive constant action replay.

4. And bill hoardings advertise products that nobody needs
   While angry of Manchester writes to complaint about
   All the repeats on T.V.
   And computer terminals report some gains
   On the values of copper and tin
   While American businessmen snap up Van Goghs
   For the price of a hospital wing.

78
Scarborough Fair/Canticle

Traditional

Arrangement & original countermelody by Paul Simon & Art Garfunkel

79
Say Yes

Words & Music by Elliott Smith

you tell me the morn-ing af-ter.

Crook-ed spin can't come to rest, I'm da-maged bad at best,

she'll de-cide what she wants. I'll prob'bly be the last to know,

no one says un-til it shows, see how it is. They

want you or they don't. Say yes.

I'm in love with the world through the eyes of a girl

who's still a-round the morn-ing af-ter.

163

80
Sisters Of Mercy

Words & Music by Leonard Cohen

Flowingly

1. Oh, the Sis-ters of Mer-cy, they are not de-par-ted or
(Verses 2-4. see block lyrics)

gone. They were

wait-ing for me when I thought that I just can't go

on. And they

brought me their com-fort and lat-er they brought me their

song. Oh, I

hope you run in-to them, you who've been trav-'ling so long.

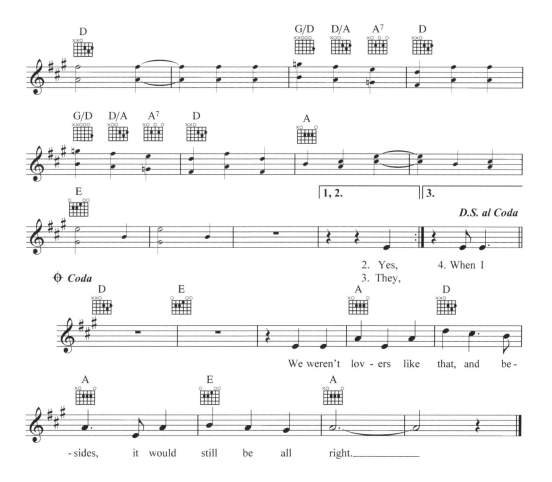

Verse 2

Yes, you who must leave everything
That you cannot control,
It begins with your family
But soon it comes round to your soul,
Well, I've been where you're hanging,
I think I can see how you're pinned,
When you're not feeling holy,
Your loneliness says that you've sinned.

Verse 3

They lay down beside me,
I made my confession to them.
They touched both my eyes
And I touched the dew on their hem.
If your life is a leaf
That the seasons tear off and condemn,
They will bind you with love
That is graceful and green as a stem.

Verse 4

When I left, they were sleeping
I hope you run into them soon,
Don't turn on the lights
You can read their address by the moon.
And you won't make me jealous
If I hear that they sweetened your night,
We weren't lovers like that
And besides, it would still be all right.
We weren't lovers like that
And besides, it would still be all right.

81
Something To Talk About

Words & Music by Damon Gough

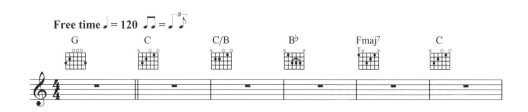

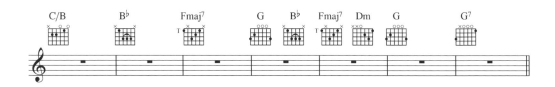

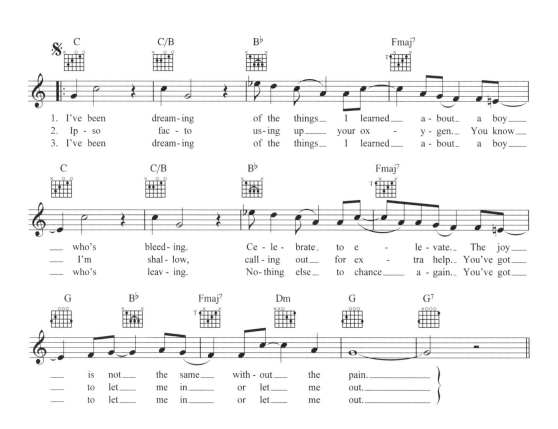

1. I've been dream-ing of the things I learned a-bout a boy who's bleed-ing. Ce-le-brate to e-le-vate. The joy is not the same with-out the pain.

2. Ip-so fac-to us-ing up your ox-y-gen. You know I'm shal-low, call-ing out for ex-tra help. You've got to let me in or let me out.

3. I've been dream-ing of the things I learned a-bout a boy who's leav-ing. No-thing else to chance a-gain. You've got to let me in or let me out.

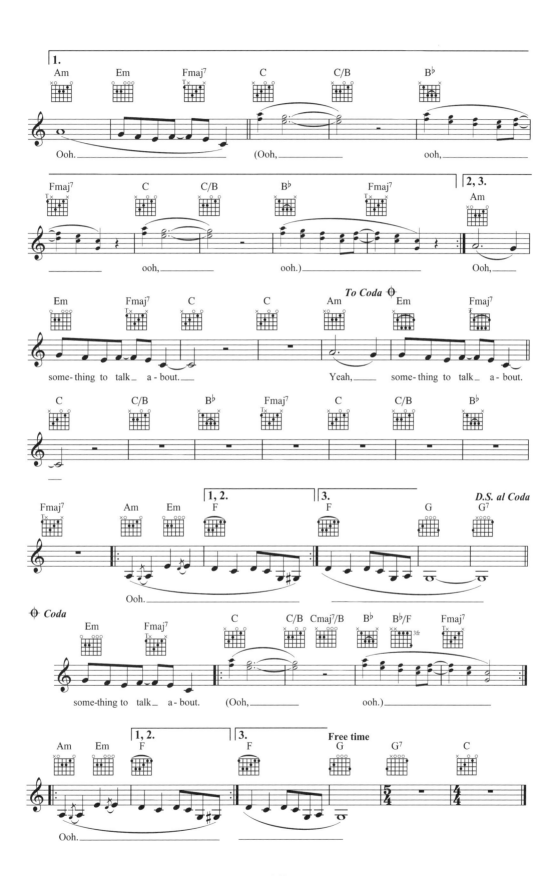

167

82
The Skye Boat Song

Traditional

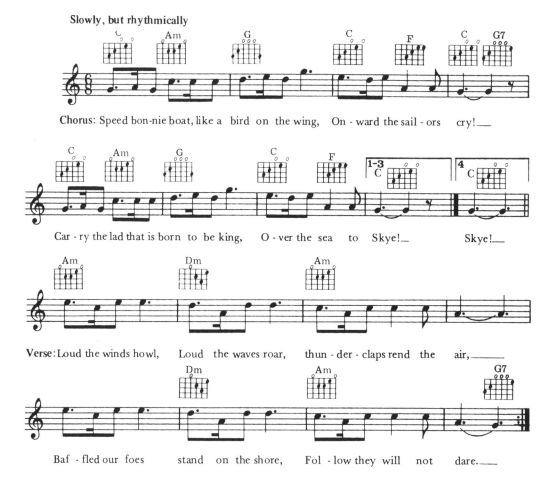

Slowly, but rhythmically

Chorus: Speed bon-nie boat, like a bird on the wing, On - ward the sail - ors cry!

Car - ry the lad that is born to be king, O - ver the sea to Skye! Skye!

Verse: Loud the winds howl, Loud the waves roar, thun - der - claps rend the air,

Baf - fled our foes stand on the shore, Fol - low they will not dare.

2. Though the waves leap, soft shall ye sleep,
Ocean's a royal bed;
Rocked in the deep, Flora will keep
Watch by your weary head.

CHORUS

3. Many's the lad fought on that day,
Well the claymore could wield
When the night came, silently lay
Dead on Culloden's field.

CHORUS

4. Burned are our homes, exile and death
Scatter the loyal men;
Yet, e'er the sword cool in the sheath,
Charlie will come again.

CHORUS

83
The Sound Of Silence

Words & Music by Paul Simon

Moderately

1. Hel - lo dark - ness, my old friend,
2. In rest -less dreams I walked a - lone
3. And in the na ked light I saw

I've come to talk to you a - gain,
nar - row streets of cob - ble - stone,
ten thou - sand peo - ple, may - be more.

Be - cause a vi - sion soft - ly
'Neath the ha - lo of a
Peo - ple talk ing with out

creep - ing,
street lamp,
speak - ing,

left it's seeds while I was sleep - ing,
I turned my col - lar to the cold and damp
peo - ple hear-ing with-out lis - ten-ing

And the vi- sion that was plant-ed in my brain still re -
When my eyes were stabbed the flash of ne-on light that split the
Peo - ple writ - ing songs that voi - ces nev-er share and no one

mains
night
dare

with - in
and touched
dis - turb

the sound of si - lence.

Verse 4
"Fools!" said I, "You do not know,
Silence like a cancer grows.
Hear my words that I might teach you,
Take my arms that I might reach you."
But my words like silent raindrops fell,
And echoed in the wells of silence.

Verse 5
And the people bowed and prayed
To the neon god they made.
And the sign flashed out its warning
In the words that it was forming.
And the signs said,
"The words of the prophets are
Written on the subway walls and tenement halls".
And whispered in the sounds of silence.

84
Stay (I Missed You)

Words & Music by Lisa Loeb

Original key: D♭ major

lo-ver's in love, and the o-ther's run a - way,_ lo-ver is crying 'cause the o-ther won't stay._

Some of us ho-ver when we weep for the o-ther who was

dy-ing since the day they were born, well. Well,

this is not___ that; I think that I'm throw-ing, but I'm

thrown._ And I thought I'd live for-e- ver, but now I'm not so sure. You try to

tell me that I'm cle- ver, that won't take me an-y-how,___ or an-y-where_ with you._

You said__ that I was na - ïve, and__

85
Tears In Heaven

Words & Music by Eric Clapton & Will Jennings

Gentle, moderate beat

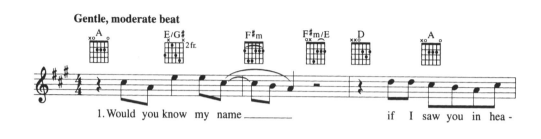

1. Would you know my name _____ if I saw you in hea-

- ven? Would you be the same _____

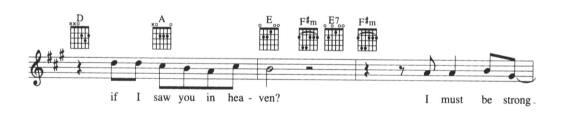

if I saw you in hea-ven? I must be strong

— and car-ry on, _____ 'cause I

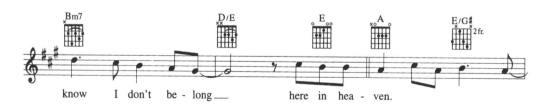

know I don't be-long _____ here in hea-ven.

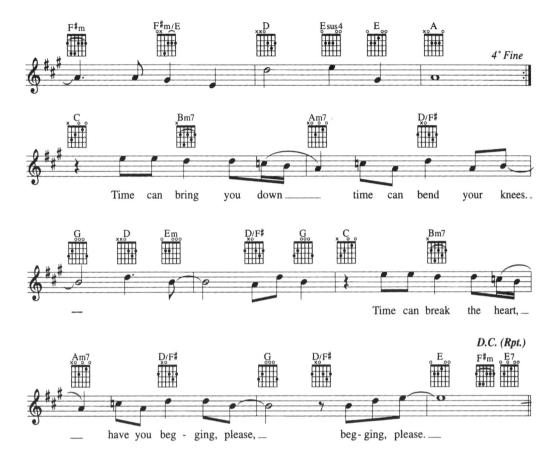

4° Fine

Time can bring you down _____ time can bend your knees. _

_ Time can break the heart, _

D.C. (Rpt.)

_ have you beg - ging, please, _ beg- ging, please. _

2.   Would you hold my hand
If I saw you in heaven?
Would you help me stand
If I saw you in heaven?
I'll find my way
Through night and day,
'Cause I know I just can't stay
Here in heaven.

Instrumental solo - 8 bars

3. *(D.C.)*   Beyond the door
There's peace, I'm sure;
And I know there'll be no more
Tears in heaven.

4. *(D.C.)*   Would you know my name
If I saw you in heaven?
Would you be the same
If I saw you in heaven?
I must be strong
And carry on,
'Cause I know I don't belong
Here in heaven.

175

86
That's Entertainment

Words & Music by Paul Weller

Guitar Capo 3rd fret.

♩ = 142

1. A pol - ice car and a scream - ing sir - en,
2. A smash of glass and the rum - ble of___ boots,
(Verses 3-6 see block lyrics)

pneu - mat - ic drill and ripped___ up con - crete.
an elec - tric train and a___ ripped up___ phone booth

A ba - by wail - ing, stray___ dog howl - ing,
Paint splat - tered walls and the cry of a tom - cat,

a screech of brakes, a lamp___
lights going out and a___

___ light blink - ing. That's en - ter - tain - ment, that's en - ter -
___ kick the in balls, I say:

1, 5.

To Coda ⊕

2, 3.

- tain - ment.

Aah,

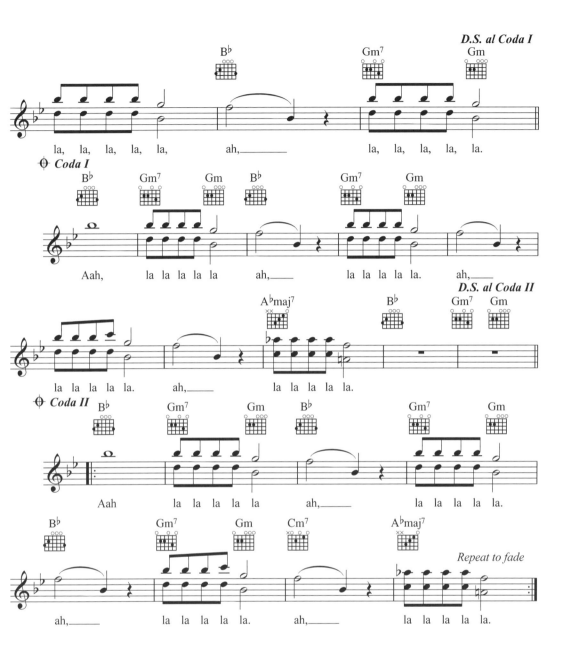

Verse 3
Days of speed and slow time Mondays,
Pissing down with rain on a boring Wednesday.
Watching the news and not eating your tea,
A freezing cold flat and damp on the walls.

Verse 4
Waking up at 6 a.m. on a cool warm morning,
Opening the windows and breathing in petrol,
An amateur band rehearsing in a nearby yard,
Watching the tele and thinking about your holidays.

Verse 5
Waking up from bad dreams and smoking cigarettes,
Cuddling a warm girl and smelling stale perfume,
A hot summers' day and sticky black tarmac,
Feeding ducks in the park and wishing you were faraway

Verse 6
Two lovers kissing amongst the scream of midnight,
Two lovers missing the tranquility of solitude,
Getting a cab and travelling on buses,
Reading the grafitti about slashed seat affairs.

87
There She Goes

Words & Music by Lee Mavers

there she goes— a - gain.— She calls my

name, pulls my train and no - one— else can feel my—

— pain.— But I— just can't— con - tain—— this

feel - in' that re - mains.————————

D.S. al Coda

Coda

There she goes—

(Call—— my name, call—— my

— There she goes.—

name. There she goes— a - gain.—— There she goes— a - gain.—

There she goes.——

— There she goes—— a - gain.)

179

88
Ticket To Ride

Words & Music by John Lennon & Paul McCartney

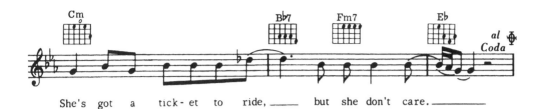

She's got a tick-et to ride, _____ but she don't care. _____

2. She   I don't know why she's rid - ing so high _____

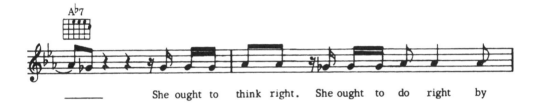

_____   She ought to think right. She ought to do right by

me.   Be - fore she gets to say-ing good-bye. _____   She ought to

think twice. She ought to do right by   me.   She

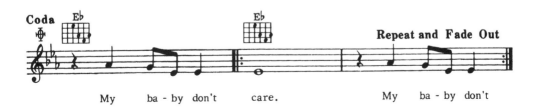

My   ba - by don't   care.   My   ba - by don't

89
Trouble

Words & Music by Guy Berryman, Jon Buckland, Will Champion & Chris Martin

183

90
Vincent

Words & Music by Don McLean

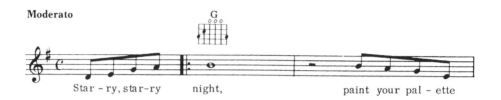

Star - ry, star-ry   night,   paint your pal - ette

blue and grey,   Look out on a   summer's day,   with

eyes that know the darkness in   my   soul. Shad-ows on the   hills,

sketch the trees and the daf-fo-dils,   Catch the breeze and the

win-ter chills, In col-ours on the snow-y li-nen land.   And now I un-der-

stand   what you tried to   say   to me,   How you suf-fered for your

san -i - ty,   How you tried to set them free. They would not lis-ten, they did

not know how, —   Perhaps they'll listen   now . For they could not   love you,

But still your love was   true,   And when no hope was left in sight on that

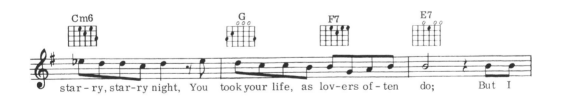
star - ry, star-ry night, You   took your life, as lov-ers of-ten   do;   But I

could have told you, Vin-cent, This world was never meant for one as beau-ti-ful as you.

91
Until It's Time For You To Go

Words & Music by Buffy Sainte-Marie

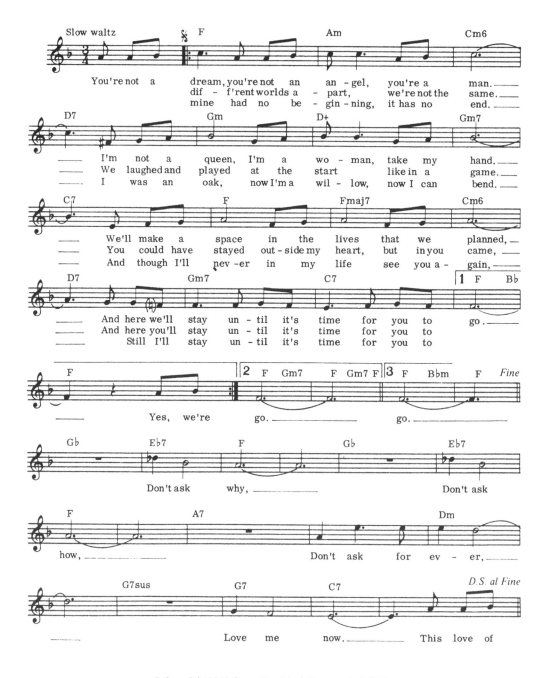

92
Waiting In Vain

Words & Music by Bob Marley

Moderately slow reggae

mf I don't wan-na wait _ in vain _ for your love. I don't wan-na wait _ in vain.

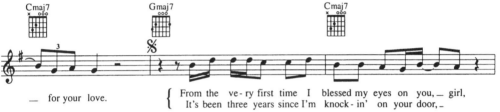

_ for your love. { From the ve - ry first time I blessed my eyes on you, _ girl,
It's been three years since I'm knock - in' on your door, _

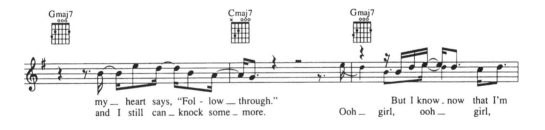

my _ heart says, "Fol - low _ through." But I know _ now that I'm
and I still can _ knock some _ more. Ooh _ girl, ooh _ girl,

way down on your line, _ but the wait - ing feel is fine. _
is it feas - i - ble, _ I wan - na know now, for _ I to knock some more?

— So don't _ treat me _ like a pup - pet on a string, _
Ya _ see, in life _ I know _ there is lots of grief, _

'cause I know how to do my thing.
but your love is my re - lief.
Don't talk __ to me __ as
Tears in my eyes burn, __

if you think __ I'm dumb. __
tears in my __ eyes burn __ while I'm wait - ing,
I wan - na know when you're gon - na come..
while I'm wait - ing for my turn. __

__ } See, I don't wan - na wait __ in vain __ for your love.

To Coda ⊕

I don't wan - na wait __ in vain __ for your love.
I don't wan - na wait in

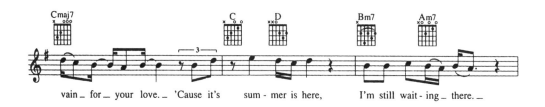

vain __ for __ your love. __ 'Cause it's sum - mer is here,
I'm still wait - ing __ there. __

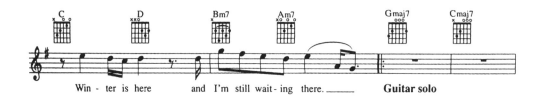

Win - ter is here and I'm still wait - ing there. _____
Guitar solo

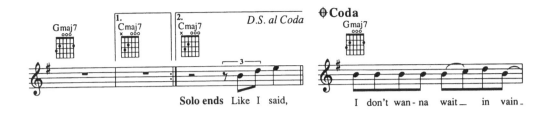

Solo ends   Like I said,   I don't wan-na wait — in vain —

— for your love.   I don't wan-na wait   in   vain — for — your love. —

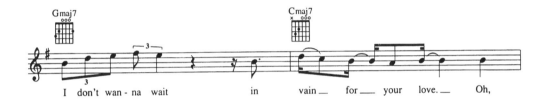

I don't wan-na wait   in   vain — for — your   love. —   Oh,

I don't wanna, I don't wanna, I don't wanna, I don't wanna, I don't wan-na wait in vain. —   No,

I don't wanna, I don't wanna, I don't wanna, I don't wan-na, I don't wan-na wait in vain. —   It's your

love that I'm — wait-ing on.   It's my love   that you're run-ning   from. —   It's your

93
The Weight

Words & Music by Robbie Robertson

1. I pulled in - to Na - za - reth, was feel - in' 'bout half - past dead. I just need some place__ where I can lay__ my head._____ "Hey, mis - ter can you tell me__ where a man might find a bed?"__ "No" was all__ he said.

2. I picked up my__ bag, I went look - ing for a place to hide, when I saw Car - men and the De - vil walk - ing side by side._____ I said, "Hey, Car - men,__ come on, let's go down - town." friend can stick a - round.

3. Go down, Miss Mos - es, there's no - thing you can say, it's just ol'__ Luke, and Luke's wait - ing on the judge - ment day._____ "Well, Luke, my friend,_____ what a - bout young An - na Lee?" stay and keep An - na Lee com - pa - ny?"

He just grinned and shook my hand,__ She said,__ "I got - ta go, but my He said, "Do me a fa - vour son, won't you

Take a load off Fan - ny,

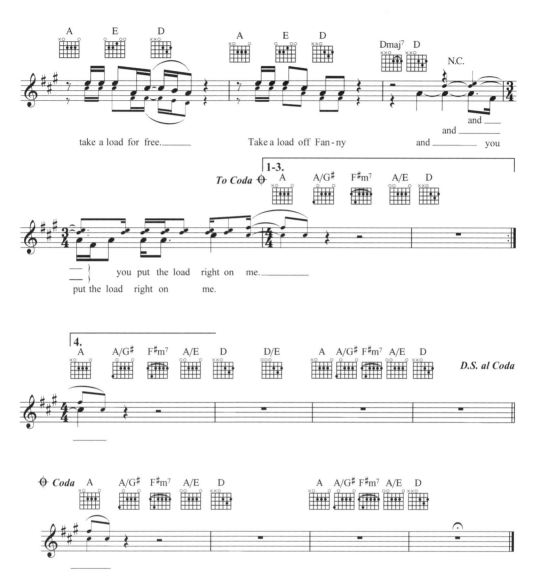

Verse 4
Crazy Chester followed me and he caught me in the fog.
He said, "I will fix your rack if you take Jack, my dog."
I said, "Wait a minute, Chester, you know, I'm a peaceful man."
He said, "That's okay boy, won't you feed him when you can?"

Take a load off, Fanny *etc.*

Verse 4
Catch a cannonball, now, to take me down the line.
My bag is sinking low and I do believe it's time
To get back to Miss Fanny, you know, she's the only one
Who sent me here with her regards for everyone.

Take a load off, Fanny *etc.*

94
What A Wonderful World

Words & Music by George Weiss & Bob Thiele

I see trees of green, red ros-es too, I see them bloom for me and you,— and I think — to my-self, What a won-der - ful world. ____ I see skies of blue and clouds of white, the bright—bles-sed day, the dark — sac-red night,—And I think — to my-self, What a won-der-ful world. ____

95
Wild Wood

Words & Music by Paul Weller

1. High tide,— mid - af - ter - noon, peo-
(Verses 2-5. see block lyrics)

- ple fly by in the traff - ic's boom.—

Know - ing— just where you're blow - ing—

get - ting to where— you— should be

go - ing.—

Verse 2:
Don't let them get you down,
Making you feel guilty about...
Golden rain will bring you riches,
All the good things you deserve now.

Verse 3:
Climbing, forever trying,
Find your way out of the wild wild wood.
Now there's no justice,
You've only yourself that you can trust in.

Verse 4:
And I said high tide, mid-afternoon,
People fly by in the traffic's boom.
Knowing just where you're blowing,
Getting to where you should be going.

Verse 5:
Day by day your world fades away,
Waiting to feel all the dreams that say.
Golden rain will bring you riches,
All the good things you deserve now.

96
Wild World

Words & Music by Cat Stevens

1. Now that I've lost ev-'ry-thing to you ___ you say you wan-na start some-thing new___
2. You know I've seen a lot of what the world can do ___ and it's break-ing my heart in two ___

___ and it's break-ing my heart ___ you're leav - ing. Ba-by, I'm griev - in'!
___ be-cause I nev-er want to see you sad, girl. Don't be a bad ___ girl.

But if you want to leave take good care, hope you have a lot of nice things to wear___
But if you want to leave take good care, hope you have a lot of nice friends out there___

___ but then a lot of nice things turn bad out there.___
___ but just re-mem-ber there's a lot of bad and be- ware. ___

Oh ba-by, ba - by it's a WILD WORLD. I'ts hard to get by ___ just up-on a

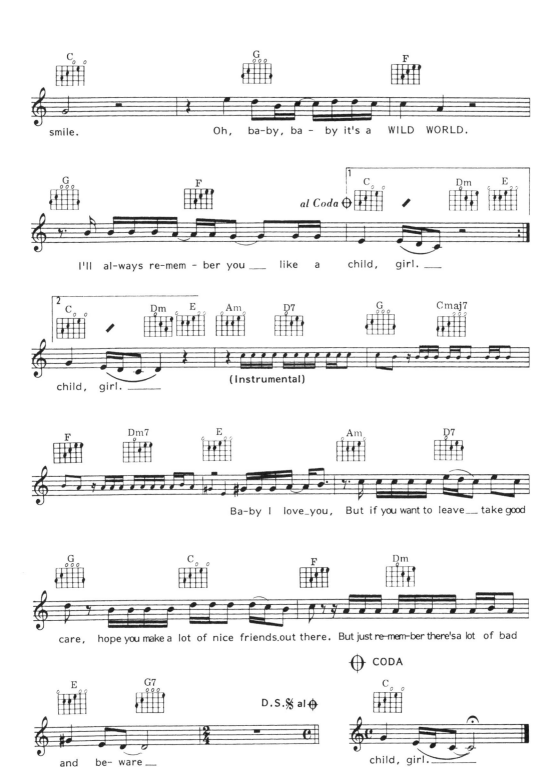

97
Wonderwall

Words & Music by Noel Gallagher

feels the way I do — a-bout you now. _____ And all _

_ the roads _ we have _ to walk _ are wind - ing, And all _

_ the lights _ that lead _ us there _ are blind - ing.

There are ma - ny things _ that I _ would like to say to you _ but I don't know how. _

_____ { Be-cause / I said } may - be _

you're gon - na be the one that saves me, _

And af - ter all _____ you're my won - der - wall. _

2. Today was gonna be the day
   But they'll never throw it back to you.
   By now you should've somehow
   Realised what you're not to do.
   I don't believe that anybody
   Feels the way I do
   About you now.

And all the roads that lead you there were winding,
And all the lights that light the way are blinding.
There are many things that I would like to say to you
But I don't know how.

98
Year Of The Cat

Words & Music by Al Stewart & Peter Wood

Moderately

On a morn-ing from a Bo-gart mov - ie, in a
does - n't give you time for ques - tions as she
morn-ing comes and you're still with her and the

coun - try where they turned back time, you go
locks up your arm in hers. And you
bus and the tour - ists are gone. And you've

stroll - ing through the crowd like Pe - ter Lor - re con - tem -
fol - low till your sense of which di - rec - tion com -
thrown a - way your choice and lost your tick - et so you

plat - ing a crime. She comes out of the sun in a silk
plete - ly dis - ap - pears. By the blue - tiled walls near the mar -
have to stay on. But the drum-beat strains of the night

dress, run - ning like a wa - ter - col - or in the rain.
ket stalls, there's a hid - den door she leads you to.
re - main in the rhy - thm of the new - born day.

Don't both-er ask-ing for ex - plan - a - tions. She'll just
'These days,' she says, ___ 'I feel my life just like a
You know some-time ___ you're bound to leave her, but for

tell you that she came in the year of the cat. ___
riv - er run - ning through, in the year of the cat.' ___
now you're gon - na stay in the year of the cat. ___

She   Well, she

looks at you ___ so cool - ly and her eyes shine like the

202

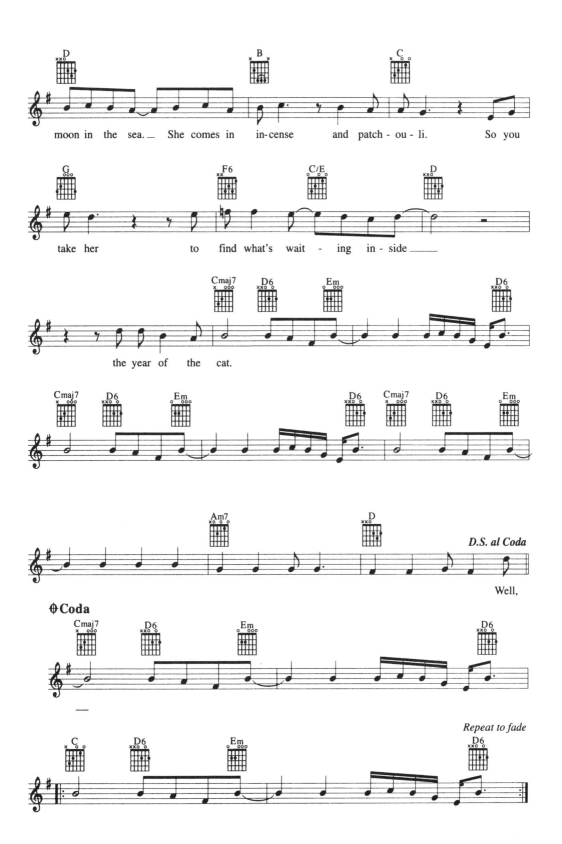

moon in the sea.__ She comes in in-cense and patch-ou-li. So you

take her to find what's wait - ing in - side _____

the year of the cat.

D.S. al Coda

Well,

✟Coda

—

Repeat to fade

99
Yellow

Words & Music by Guy Berryman, Jon Buckland, Will Champion & Chris Martin

100
You're So Vain

Words & Music by Carly Simon

-votte and — all the girls — dreamed that they'd — be your part-ner, they'd-
me, I — had some dreams, _ _ they were clouds — in my cof-fee, clouds_
with some un - der-world spy — or the wife — of a close friend, wife-

CHORUS

— be your part - ner and
— in my cof - fee and   You're — so — vain, —
— of a close — friend and

you prob-b'ly think this song is a - bout — you. You're — so — vain _

I'll bet you think this song is a - bout — you. Don't — you? Don't _

1,2.   3.

— you? — You   — you? — You're — so — vain —
          Well, I

Repeat to fade

— you prob-b'ly think this song is a - bout — you. —

207

101
Yesterday

Words & Music John Lennon & Paul McCartney

7 8 9